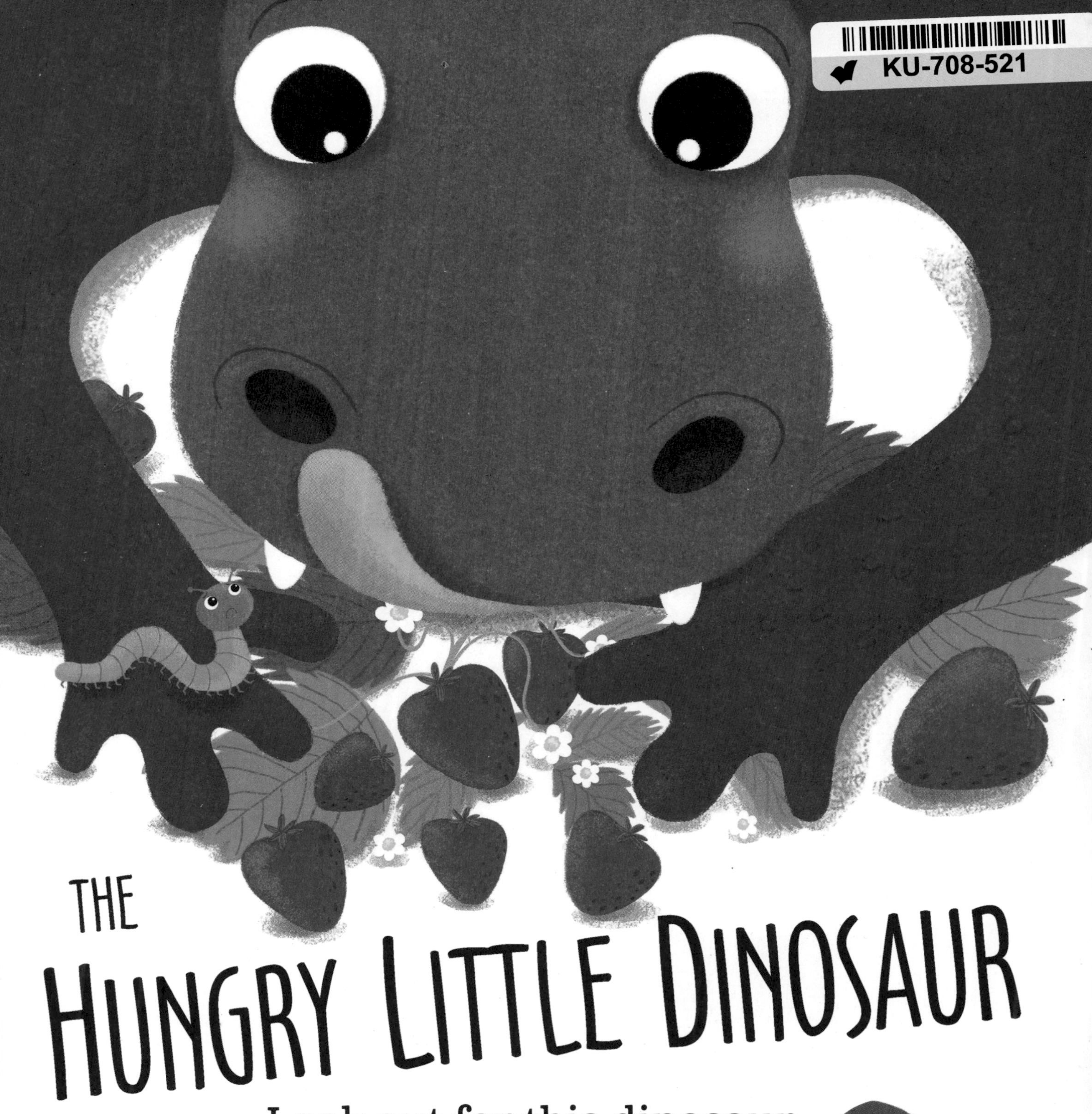

KU-708-521

THE HUNGRY LITTLE DINOSAUR

Look out for this dinosaur
as you read the story.

Fruitysaurus is a fruit-loving, fruit-gobbling, fruit-fanatic! He just loves fruit, no one else gets any to eat when he's around.

I think I can hear Fruitysaurus coming.
This won't last long with him around!

Fruitysaurus loves bananas so much, he eats them by the bunch.
Er, excuse me!
He'll turn into a banana!

Munch!
Munch!

There is no fruit that Fruitysaurus does not like. He eats them ALL!

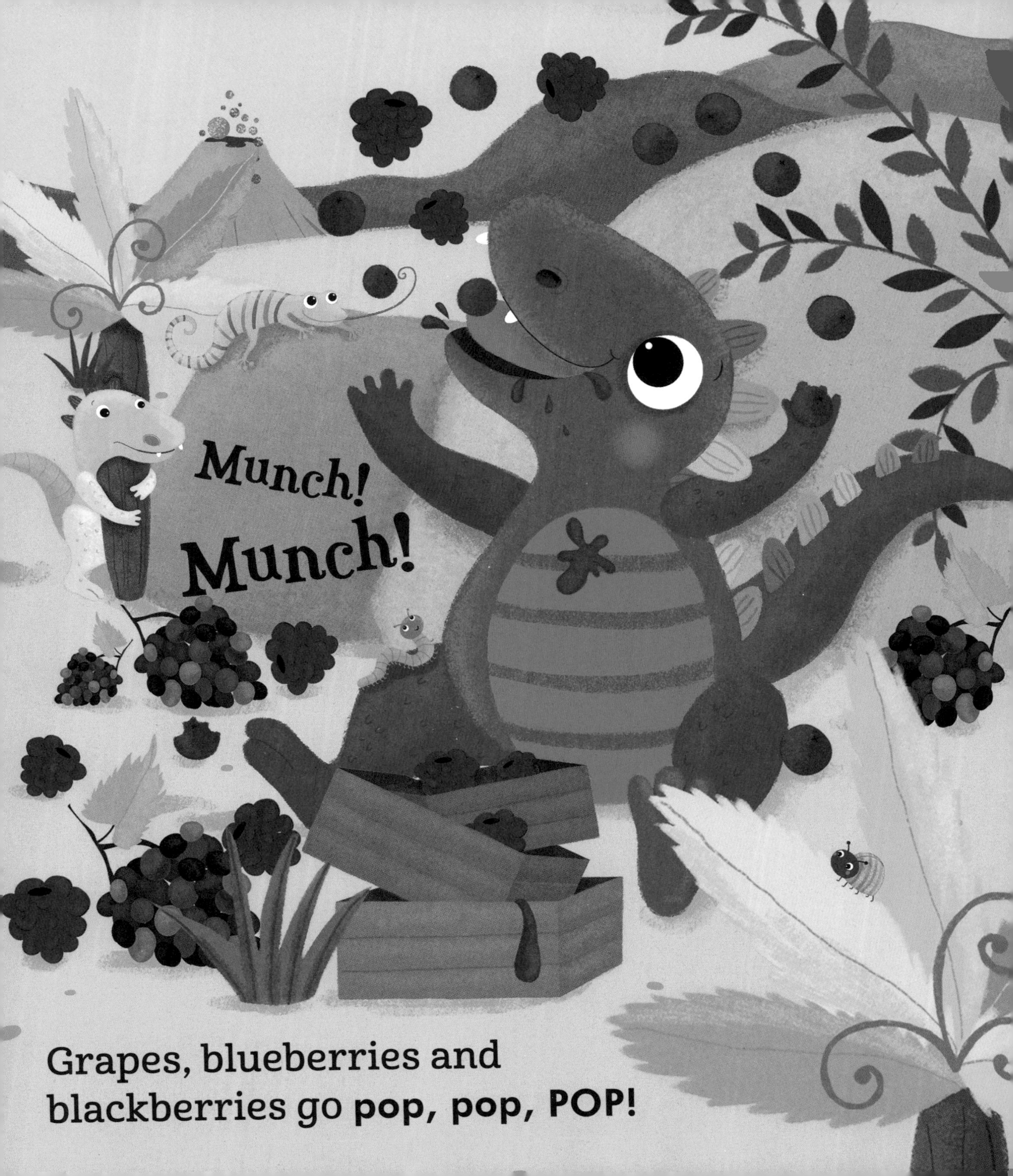

Grapes, blueberries and
blackberries go **pop, pop, POP!**

Apples, kiwis and pears are next,
he just can't stop!

I'm sorry baby,
he has eaten
them all.
How rude!

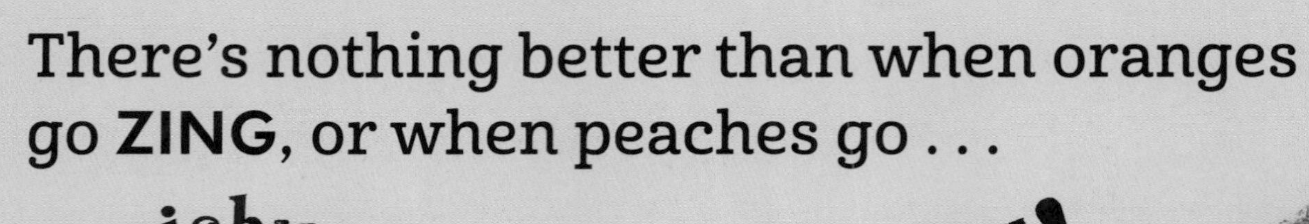

There's nothing better than when oranges go **ZING**, or when peaches go . . .

squishy-squish-**SQUISH!**

Get out quick!

Yikes!

Munch! Munch!

He'll climb up high to **CRUNCH** tasty coconuts . . .

. . . and shake them up to make a delicious milkshake!

. . . or sneak down low
to gulp on strawberries.

You're eating them all?
Munch! Munch!

Fruitysaurus really loves fruit but he's not the only one who likes to eat it. His friends are sad and cross and tired of his greedy ways.

Can Fruitysaurus think of a way to say sorry?

Fruitysaurus has a plan to say he's sorry.

Of course it involves fruit!
How could it not?

It's a fruity pizza party for all his friends. What a sweet idea!
Munch!
Munch!
Munch!

There's nothing better
than munching together.
Munch with me!
Thank you!
Munch!
Munch!

The dinosaurs have forgiven Fruitysaurus. Everyone can enjoy the fruit!

The Hungry Little Dinosaur

A LAUGHING LOBSTER BOOK 978-1-910764-65-7
Published in Great Britain by Laughing Lobster, an imprint of Centum Publishing Ltd.
This edition published 2022.

1 3 5 7 9 10 8 6 4 2

© 2022 Laughing Lobster, an imprint of Centum Publishing Ltd. All Rights Reserved.

Illustrations by Sophie Hanton.

No part of this publication may be reproduced, stored in a retrieval system, or transmitted in any form or by any means, electronic, mechanical, photocopying, recording or otherwise, without the prior permission of the publishers.

Laughing Lobster, an imprint of Centum Publishing Ltd, 20 Devon Square, Newton Abbot, Devon, TQ12 2HR, UK. Centum Publishing Ltd, 9/10 Fenian St, Dublin 2, D02 RX24, Ireland

books@centumpublishingltd.co.uk

LAUGHING LOBSTER, CENTUM PUBLISHING LIMITED Reg. No. 08497203

A CIP catalogue record for this book is available from the British Library.

Printed in China.